Zero Z
Ty

David Walke

I TY

CRASH!

The door smashed open. The troopers crashed into the room. They had guns. The old man turned to face them. He shouted to the girl.

"Run, Zia! Run to the space-jet!" he said.

"Stop or we will fire!" yelled a trooper.

"Come with me, Father!" the girl called.

"Get to the space-jet," said the old man, "I will follow you."

The troopers ran towards him. The old man held up his hand to them. They stopped. The old man took hold of a small silver stone that hung around his neck. The stone shone in his fingers. He looked deep into the eyes of the troopers.

The troopers dropped their guns. They tried to cover their eyes. The old man seemed to burn into their minds.

"No! Stop! Stop!" they screamed.

Suddenly the old man turned and ran to the space-jet. He jumped into the cabin with the girl. Zia fired the engines and the space-jet sped away. It skimmed down the long cave and blasted out into space.

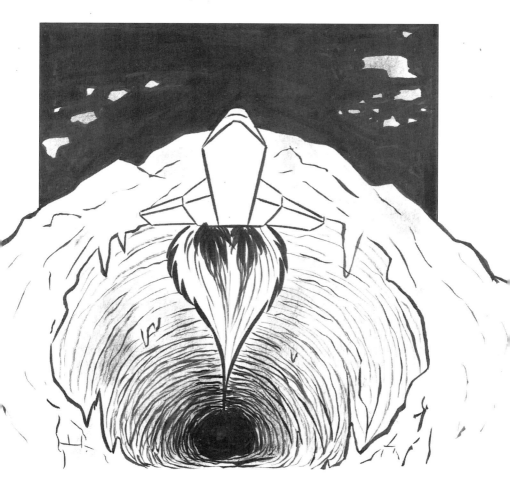

2 ZEK

Zek screamed at his troopers.

"Where is he? Where is Ty, the magic-man? You have let him get away! I want him! I want his power!"

The troopers lay on the floor. They held their hands to their eyes. They groaned with pain. Zek grabbed an intercom. He screamed into it.

"You will not get away, Ty. I will find you. I will destroy you."

On the space-jet the old man heard Zek's words. He looked at the girl.

"Don't worry. Zek will not find us. We are safe now," he said.

Zia said, "Yes, Father." But she did not believe him.

3 HIT

The shot hit the space-jet and sent it spinning over and over. Zia screamed as Ty pulled hard on the controls. Across the Zero Zone, Starhunter got the distress call.

"Help us! Help us!" cried Zia over the intercom.

"This is Starhunter" said Rikk. "We hear you."

"Please hurry! Zek is coming for us!" cried Zia.

"Hold on, space-jet. We're on our way," said Rikk.

Lin flicked the controls. Starhunter shot forward. The ship streaked towards the distress call.

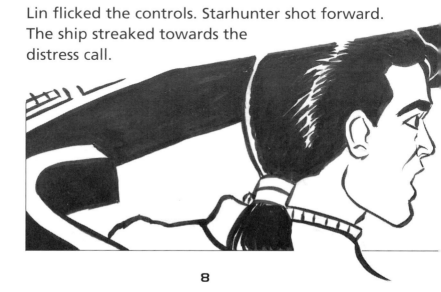

4 BLAST

Shap watched his screen for the space-jet.
Suddenly he saw it.

"There it is, Captain," he said.

"It's in a real mess," said Lin.

"It's going to blow any second," said Rikk.

"We've got to get them out of there,"
said Shap.

"Get Starhunter in close," said Rikk. "OP2, take the rescue suits to Zia and her father."

Starhunter moved slowly across to the space-jet. The little robot flew out. When he got to the jet, Ty and Zia put on the rescue suits. Suddenly, there was a bang and flames spat out of a hole in the jet.

"Hurry! It's going to blow!" yelled Shap.

"OP2, get them back here!" called Rikk.

As Ty zipped the rescue suit up he felt for the silver stone.

"Wait! Wait!" he cried.

"There's no time!" called Shap.

"Get out of there NOW!" said Rikk.

Ty and Zia grabbed onto OP2. The robot flew
across to Starhunter. Another blast of flame
shot from the space-jet. Zia and Ty dropped
down into the starship.

Suddenly the space-jet blew up. The ball of fire
rocked Starhunter. The blast hit OP2 full on as
he tried to get into the starship. Bits from the
jet ripped into the little robot. He fell back into
the starship with a crash. He smashed down
onto the deck.

5 LOST

Rikk and Lin came onto the deck.

"Thank you for saving us," said Ty. He took Rikk's hand and bowed his head.

"But look at your robot," said Zia. She bent down to OP2.

"Oh, no! What happened?" cried Lin.

"The blast got him," said Zia. "I'm sorry."

Rikk lifted the little robot onto a workbench. He was all burned. Some of his control panel had gone. Something had punched a hole into his side.

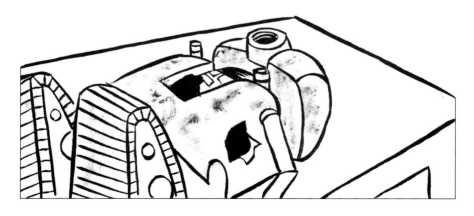

Rikk quickly took some leads from the computer. He clipped them on to OP2.

"What are you doing, Captain?" asked Zia.

"OP2 is a very clever robot," said Rikk.

"He can fix himself," said Lin. "He has the power."

"My father has powers, too," said Zia.

Ty looked at her. He felt for the silver stone round his neck. It had gone.

6 POWER

"My father is a magic-man," said Zia. "He too has the power. He fights for good."

"Tell me about Zek," said Rikk.

"Zek is evil," said Zia. "He has many troopers and many starfighters."

"He wants me," said Ty. "He wants my power so he can steal and destroy."

Then Zia said, "Thank you for helping us. I'm sorry about OP2."

"He'll be OK," said Shap.

They turned to the workbench. OP2 lay still. The computer sent signals into his body. Suddenly the lights on his control panel flashed on. Lin smiled.

"Soon he'll be as good as new," she said.

"Everything is looking good," said Shap.

"Not so good," said Rikk.

He pointed to the window. They looked out. Starhunter was not alone. Starfighters were coming at them fast.

"What's going on?" asked Shap.

"It's Zek," said Ty.

7 FIGHTERS

Rikk jumped into his seat and hit the controls.
He put the nose of the starship down.
Starhunter dived past the fighters at full blast.

"Let's give Zek a run for his money," he yelled.

"Cannons ready!" cried Lin.

A starfighter flashed across them. Starhunter's
cannons blasted. The starfighter went up in a
ball of flame. Rikk pulled the ship round. The
cannons fired again and blasted another
fighter. It spun over and over and blew up in a
flash of red.

"Two starfighters coming in," cried Shap.

"I'll pull Starhunter around. Fire!" said Rikk.

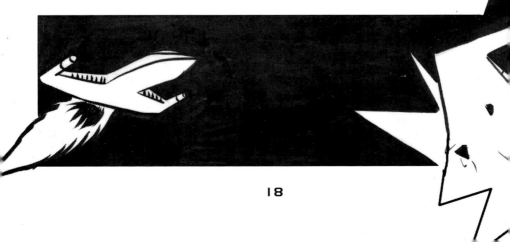

Starhunter came up and round. Lin fired.
The first starfighter was hit and blew up.
The second starfighter fired back. The shot
clipped Starhunter's wing. The ship rocked
and turned over. Another starfighter fired.
Then another starfighter came in.

"It's no good!" said Shap.

"We're not going to make it," said Lin.

"There's got to be a way out," said Rikk.

The intercom came on.

"There's no way out," said a voice.

It was Zek.

"You are trapped!"

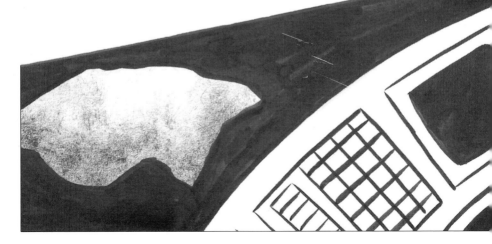

The crew looked at the screen. Zek had got them. A ring of fighters flew around Starhunter.

There was nowhere to go.

8 TRAPPED

Nobody spoke. They looked out at the fighters. Their guns were aimed at Starhunter. The intercom came on.

"Give Ty to me or I will destroy you," said Zek.

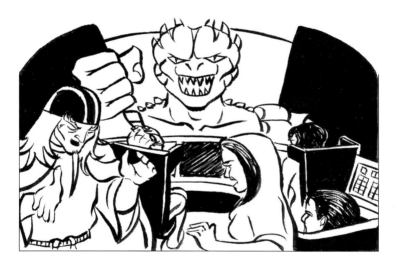

"Father, use your power! Use the stone! Stop Zek!" said Zia.

"The stone is gone," Ty said.

"Gone? Where is it?" said Zia.

"It was lost on the space-jet. OP2 saved my life but he could not save the stone," said Ty.

"So you cannot use your power," said Zia.

"I must stop Zek. I must save you," said Ty.

"No, Father! No! Not without the stone!" said Zia.

"What is this stone?" asked Rikk.

"The stone gives my father power. The stone gives my father life," said Zia.

"My life is nothing now," said Ty.

He turned to OP2. The robot lay on the workbench. His control panel was working now. The holes in his metal skin were fixed. Only one big hole in his side was left.

Ty turned back. He looked at Zek's fighters. He held out his hand to them.

"Father, do not do this," said Zia. She had tears in her eyes.

"I must try," said Ty.

Slowly he turned to the fighters. He held up his hand. Nothing happened. Ty closed his eyes. Still nothing happened. Nothing at all.

9 THE STONE

Ty fell back. He lay on the deck. Zia went to him.

"Father!" she cried.

The crew looked down at Ty. He seemed to start to fade away. The stone had gone. His power had gone.

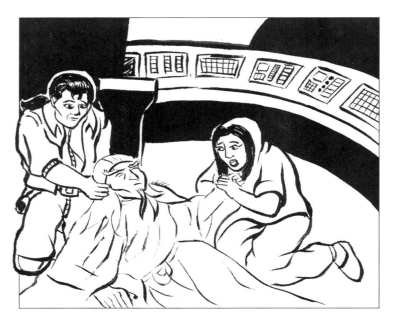

Suddenly OP2 moved. The computer had done its work. OP2 was fixed. All that was left was a hole in his side. As the robot moved, something fell out of the hole.

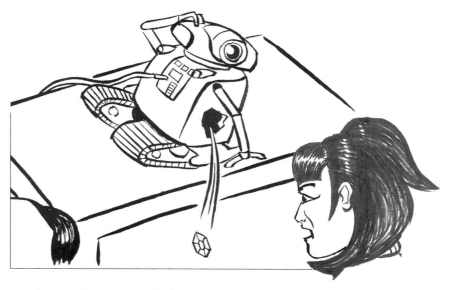

"What's that?" said Shap.

"It's a stone," said Lin. She picked it up. It glinted in the light.

"A stone?" said Zia. "Let me see!"

Lin handed it to her.

"This is it!" said Zia. "This is my father's stone! We can save him!"

10 GO

Zia went to Ty. She put the stone into his hands. His eyes flicked open.

"You found the stone," he said.

"OP2 found it," said Zia.

"You have saved my life again, my little friend," said Ty.

The lights on OP2's control panel flashed.

"Now for Zek," Ty said.

He stood and turned to the fighters. He held up his hand. There was a flash as one of the fighters went up in a ball of flame. Ty turned to each fighter. Rikk grabbed the intercom.

"Zek, get out of here or you'll end up the same way!" he yelled.

Another fighter blew up in a flash of fire. Then one by one the other starfighters turned and fled.

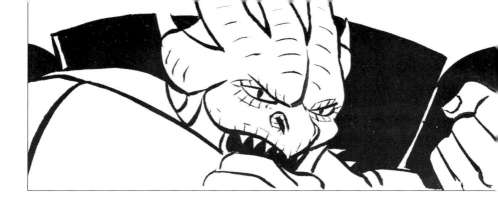

"Come back!" screamed Zek. "Come back!"

"Go with them, Zek, or I'll blast you out of space!" said Ty.

"Aah!" screamed Zek.

There was a flash from Zek's engines. Then his fighters turned and blasted away.

"OK. Let's get out of here," said Rikk.

He slipped into his seat. Lin flicked the controls. The engines fired and Starhunter blasted off deep into the Zero Zone.

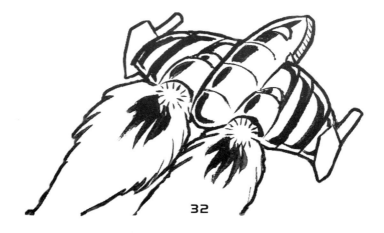